Improve your sight-r

A piece a week

Grade 6

Paul Harris

FABER *ff* MUSIC

Introduction

Why?

One of the main reasons why so many young pianists can't sight-read is simply because they don't spend enough time actually looking at, and processing, notation. It's not uncommon to spend many weeks (perhaps even longer) learning just one or two pieces. These pieces are really learnt by ear and tactile memory – the notation becomes more of an aide-memoire, symbols that nudge kinaesthetic memory.

So we need to encourage students to spend more time literally looking at notation! That's the purpose of this book of pieces. It's a one-a-week or, possibly, one-every-two-weeks collection of pieces that will be especially useful when a student is moving towards an exam.

Not actually sight-reading

These pieces are not to be sight-read: the idea is to learn one piece each week so that students are constantly having to process new notation in a comfortable time frame. They have to actually LOOK at new music more often and so will become less nervous and more able to deal with it. It will begin to take the fear and panic out of reading and notation.

Standard

Each piece is deliberately much quicker to learn than typical Grade 6-level pieces. Each is built on a different (and interesting) pianistic idea, exploring colourful sonorities and the whole range of the piano.

Presenting the piece

When setting students off to work at a piece, should you play it to them first? In general, encourage them to work out the ideas for themselves. It's okay to play a few bars, but try to avoid playing the whole piece – it's amazing what many students will pick up by ear and by watching your fingers!

Practice

It's important that students practise these pieces regularly – every day, ideally – so that they are regularly reading notation. A new piece each week for 27 weeks before an exam will make a huge difference.

Ingredients

Each piece is based on a small number of ideas – particular rhythms and note patterns – but has quite a number of dynamics and other markings: these are very important. Students very rarely manage to include dynamics and other markings when sight-reading in exams. Doing so takes practice and these pieces will give them that opportunity!

Fingering

There is a certain amount of fingering marked. It's very important that students learn that the point of fingering is simply to get your hand to the right place so that the notes can be played. Once that point is understood it all becomes so much more achievable. It's very important that this connection is made. Do encourage students to pencil in their own additional fingerings or even change notated fingerings if they find their own more preferable.

Pulse

It's interesting that many students really don't understand the importance of pulse. By playing new pieces regularly and thinking about the pulse each time, there is much more chance that the concept will be understood and then applied successfully to actual sight-reading! Insist that students always think about and set the pulse before they begin playing.

It's essential that the pulse they set is manageable. If it's too fast and the pulse is constantly unstable, the concept will take much longer to fully digest. Metronome markings are given but only as broad suggestions.

Style, expression and character

Encourage students to think about and explore style, expression and character. What is the best tempo? How will they interpret the dynamics to get the best effect? Can they add extra crescendo and diminuendo to give more shape and direction? What sort of touch is required? Is it best to play strictly in time or would a degree of freedom in the pulse be appropriate? How will they communicate the piece's 'message'? And so on …

Performance

These pieces also make ideal concert items. Students, occasionally, may like to perform small selections, creating their own miniature suites from 3 or 4 pieces.

Final word

I hope you and your students will enjoy working through *A Piece a Week* Grade 6 – especially the sounds, rhythms, structures and characters of the music. And I hope they will become less intimidated by notation and learn to look forward to reading new material on their own.

Paul Harris

Contents

With thanks to Tim Bowers, Andrew Eales, Ann Priestley and Flora Tzannetaki.

Music processed by Donald Thomson
Cover and page design by Susan Clarke
Printed in England by Caligraving Ltd
All rights reserved

ISBN10: 0-571-54139-9
EAN13: 978-0-571-54139-3

To buy Faber Music publications or to find out about the full range of titles available
please contact your local music retailer or Faber Music sales enquiries:
Faber Music Ltd, Burnt Mill, Elizabeth Way, Harlow CM20 2HX
Tel: +44 (0) 1279 82 89 82   Fax: 44 (0) 1279 82 89 83
sales@fabermusic.com   fabermusicstore.com

Ballade Parisienne

5

Bach goes to Staffa*

* Fingal's Cave is on the Isle of Staffa

6

River

7

Invention

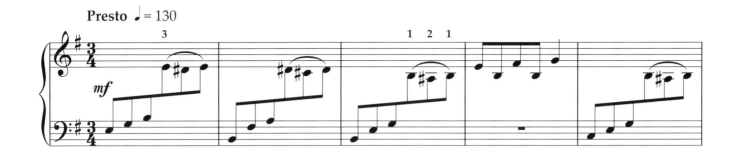

Aria

9

Sticking*

Con moto (percussively) ♩ = 60

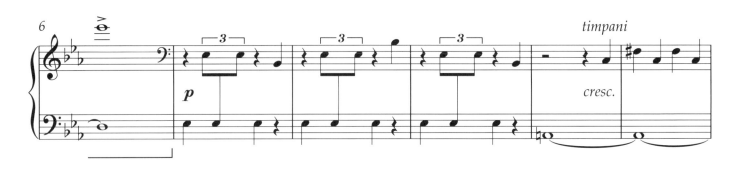

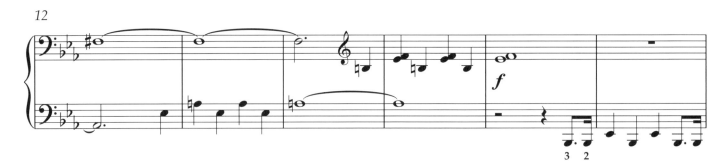

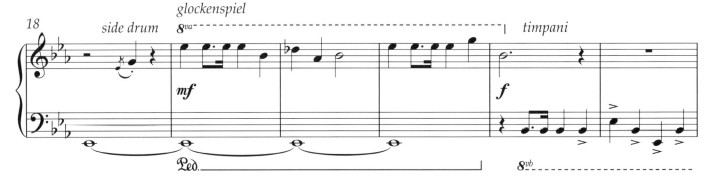

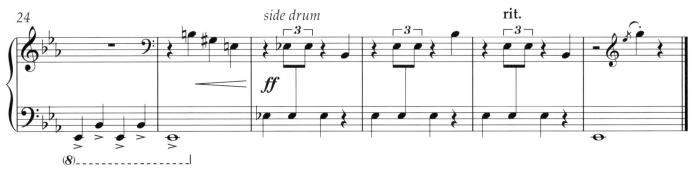

* *Sticking* refers to the way percussionists use their sticks

10

Haltz

Spirited, with swing ♩ = 110

11

Contemplation

Toccata

Oceans deep

Skydive

With a huge adrenaline rush ♩ = 120

molto rit.

15

A night in Rio

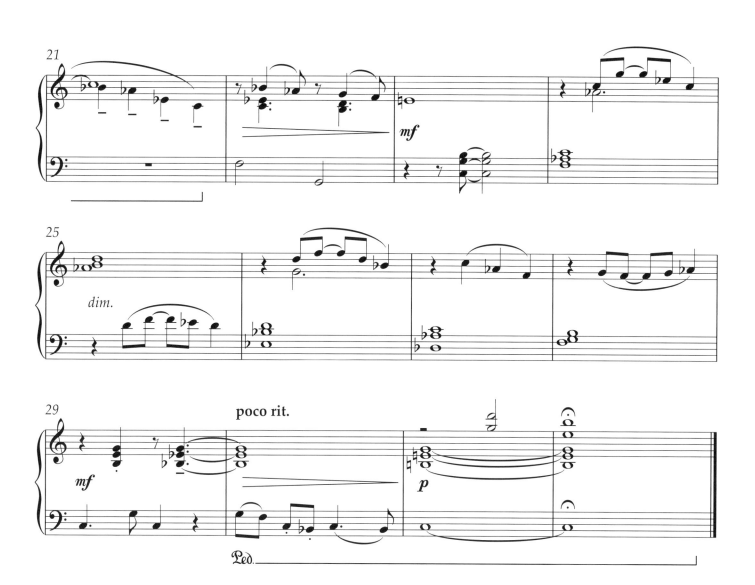

Miniscule mazurka

Cosmic dust

Spanner in the works

This is no laughing matter

This is a laughing matter

Minuet for Miss Sara Bande

Nocturne

Cat

24

The flight of the phoenix

Take it easy

Frenzy

(Hold these notes down silently throughout)

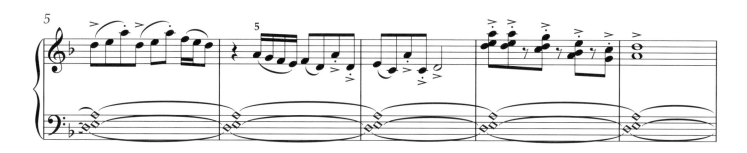

Danse macabre

Agent TX9 undercover in Havana

Dodgems

Shimmering

The big finale